Play with me

including children with autism in mainstream primary schools

Isabel Cottinelli Telmo

All the children in our school are different: some are very tall, some are very short and some wear glasses. One boy can't speak English very well because he comes from another country where they speak a different language. But this year we have John who's very different from all of us. The teacher says that he has autism.

Autism isn't an illness but a 'developmental disorder.'

This means that John doesn't grow up like us in the same way. He doesn't talk like the other school children and he doesn't learn words if we teach them to him, like we do with Alex. The teacher says that we have to be patient with him and understand why he can't do the same as we do.

John doesn't answer when we speak to him, or else he repeats what we say.
We ask him 'Do you want to come and play ball?'
He answers 'Do you want to come and play ball?'

We used to think that he was making fun of us, but he's not.
The teacher says that it's his way of saying yes. But
afterwards, when he comes and plays, it's very funny because
he doesn't throw the ball like us. He doesn't understand that he
has to score a goal in the net. Do you know what he does
instead? He bites the ball or rolls it around in his hand.

The teacher tells us to play with him so that he learns how to do it. She says th
we should throw him the ball and keep trying so that he throws the ball back
us. We have to do this over and over again every day until he can do it.

When we're racing toy cars, John grabs hold of them. But he doesn't race them – he bangs them on the ground, bites them or throws them against the wall. He does the same with the other toys as well.

And do you know what's even odder?

John does the same thing with his own toys, even his favourites. If he damages them he doesn't mind. He picks up the bits and throws them onto the ground or rolls them around in his hand.

We like collecting bottle tops, or marbles or tattoos. Then we swap them with other children.

John collects very silly things. Just look at what he has in his trouser pocket – do you know what he's got? Banana skins and peach stones. Sometimes John goes round with bits of paper in his hand and, if somebody takes them away from him or he loses them, he screams so much that we have to go and look for them. He only stops screaming when we've found them.

And sometimes no one knows why he's screaming. It's his way of talking and it's just that we don't understand.

John knows how to take messages to people at school but he has to be told one message at a time.

If you tell him two or three messages at once he can get mixed up and forgets them all. John does this because he finds it difficult to understand what people tell him.

When we're sitting down in class, John sometimes gets up and leaves the room. If we did the same thing the teacher would get cross. When we ask the teacher about this she says that we have to be patient and little by little persuade him to stay in his seat.

John gets up and walks away because he finds it hard to stay sitting down for a long time. He needs to move around and walk about more often than we do. He needs more space to move about in.

We have to understand him and keep on persuading him to stay seated for longer. Every day he manages to stay seated a little longer at the table.

John is not afraid of things which could hurt us. When he's out in the street he walks in between the cars and could get run over.

We have to teach him what we have already learnt. If we always cross on the pedestrian crossings or with the little green man he learns to do what we do.

John often sits on a chair or stands up in a corner far away from us. When he does this at playtime, he covers his ears with his hands and sometimes screams.

The teacher says that he hears things in a different way from us. When he hears a lot of noise he gets very anxious, and covers his ears so he can't hear. It's a bit strange. If he doesn't like noise why does he scream? He makes even more noise!

It's best for us to leave him alone or take him away from the noisiest place. He doesn't like Tom and Jerry videos because they are so noisy.

But at other times John is afraid of things which don't frighten anyone else. He's even afraid of umbrellas! If someone opens an umbrella he starts screaming.

These fears usually only last a few months. But it's best if we don't do things which scare him because otherwise he can get so worked up and worried that he ends up biting and scratching himself until he bleeds. This is because he doesn't understand things like we do.

John screams because he can't talk. Screaming is his way of saying something. He can say some words but doesn't answer us properly when we speak to him.

We say, 'Come here, John' and he answers, 'The car's yellow.' That's strange because there's no car.

The teacher says that he learns sentences and uses them later without understanding why. We have to teach him to reply. We can also show him drawings of what we want and then he understands better.

The teacher has some cards which she gives to him so that he can let her know when he wants to go to the toilet or eat.

When we like a friend we give them a hug.

Do you know what John does instead? He bites them or hits them. It's his way of saying that he likes them. We have to teach him not to do this and show him what he should do. We also have to show him that we're cross when he hits us.

But we have to be careful not to hit him back otherwise he thinks it's a game and won't stop hitting or biting. We all have to agree to do the same thing so that he understands better.

Another very strange thing is when we're crying.

We cry because we've hurt ourselves or we're feeling sad. Everyone else feels sorry for us. But John laughs instead and the more we cry the more he laughs.

The teacher says that John doesn't understand that we're sad and thinks that we are messing around and joking to make the others laugh.

We have to show him clearly that we're sad.

But John can be very sweet.
He can climb trees better than
a monkey – it's amazing!

He climbs much faster than us.
Sometimes it's dangerous because he
doesn't understand that he might fall.

Also he runs away when he wants
to avoid something he doesn't
like doing. He is faster than the
speed of light.

John draws very nicely. Do you know what Pokémon is? He does Pokémon drawings all the time and they're very good.

He's the best in the class at drawing. The other day he wanted to take one of the children's T-shirts off because there was a Pokémon picture on it.

The worst thing of all is when John ruins our pictures. All of a sudden he scribbles all over them or tears them up and we don't have time to stop him. It upsets us because our pictures are so good!

But he doesn't do this on purpose. Maybe he wants to draw as well. When he does it, it's best to give him a sheet of paper to draw on.

Something else we don't like is that he sometimes spoils our games and our toys. But we have to understand that he doesn't know what he's doing.

We think it's very unfair that the teacher doesn't get cross with him. If we did the same thing she would be very cross. Do you know why? Because we know that we're being naughty and he doesn't really understand what he's doing.

John doesn't like things to be moved.

He always wants to sit on the same chair and at the same table. If someone else sits in his place he gets very cross and very very worked up. He sulks and that is his way of saying that he doesn't like changing places.

He also likes to do the same things at the same time of day.

If the gym teacher can't come to the class, John won't take his tracksuit off until the gym session is over.

If he can't go to the swimming pool because it's raining he gets very worked up. He can't understand why we're not doing the usual things.

Do you know that he even goes to the bus stop to wait for the school bus on a Sunday?

His family have to explain to him that they stay at home on Sundays too.

Now they try to organise something special for him to do on Sundays, like going for a walk after lunch.

When we're laughing about something John starts laughing so much that he just can't stop and gets very excited. It's even really hard for the teacher to get him to stop.

It's better if we calm down before he gets to that stage.

There's one thing that I find difficult about John.

It's when he looks at me and doesn't actually look me in the eyes. He seems to be looking at something else although he's looking at me. I end up thinking that I've turned into the Invisible Man.

There's one thing about John that I like very much.

John can play the piano very well. I wish I could play as well as him.

It's nice because this shows that we're all really different and we have to understand that we can do some things quite well and other things very badly.

Children with autism like playing with us and they are fun to play with. John likes me and I like him too. I really like helping him and teaching him things. When he learns to do something new we're all very happy and he is too.

If there's a child with autism in your school, learn to understand how they behave. They may not do things as well as John, but they may be able to do many of the things you've read about in this book. You may already know that they may not even know how to talk. Sometimes maybe they speak in a strange way.

You need to understand that they can't play like other children if they don't teach him how to play. Sometimes they may hit out or sulk or scream. They'll learn some things very well, but they won't understand other things if you don't help them a lot.

Original title: Bricomigo – para a inclusao das crincas con autismo nas escolas do 1. ciclo
(Play with me – For the integration of children with autism into primary schools)
Author: Isabel Cottinelli Telmo
Publisher: APPDA, Lisbon
Drawings: Ferdinanda Vaz
Graphic Design: Marta Pardal Monteiro
ISBN: 972-98512-1-2
National Book Catalogue Number: 188459/02
Printed by: Multitema
Print run: 2000 copies

I am very grateful to 3rd year pupil Maria Gorjão Henriques who looked at the text from a child's point of view.